Beatles
Accordion Songbook

A Hard Day's Night **6**

All You Need Is Love **3**

Eight Days A Week **10**

Eleanor Rigby **13**

Hey Jude **16**

I Want To Hold Your Hand **19**

Lucy In The Sky With Diamonds **22**

Michelle **26**

Norwegian Wood **32**

Nowhere Man **29**

Ob-La-Di, Ob-La-Da **36**

Strawberry Fields Forever **41**

With A Little Help From My Friends **46**

Yesterday **44**

Wise Publications
London/New York/Paris/Sydney/Copenhagen/Madrid

Exclusive Distributors:

Music Sales Limited
8/9 Frith Street,
London W1V 5TZ, England.

Music Sales Pty Limited
120 Rothschild Avenue,
Rosebery, NSW 2018,
Australia.

Order No. NO90661
ISBN 0-7119-6394-0
This book © Copyright 1998 by Wise Publications

Book design by Chloë Alexander
Compiled by Peter Evans
Music arranged by Pete Lee
Music processed by Enigma Music Production Services

Printed in the United Kingdom by
Printwise (Haverhill) Limited, Haverhill, Suffolk.

Cover photography by George Taylor
Instrument featured: Trevani Francesco, made in Castelfidardo, Italy
by Guerrini & Figli. Kindly loaned by Trevani, 14 Mapledale Avenue,
Croydon CR0 5TB, England.
Cover photograph of The Beatles courtesy of Camera Press London.

Your Guarantee of Quality
As publishers, we strive to produce every book to the highest commercial standards.
The music has been freshly engraved and the book has been carefully designed to minimise
awkward page turns and to make playing from it a real pleasure.
Particular care has been given to specifying acid-free, neutral-sized paper made from pulps
which have not been elemental chlorine bleached. This pulp is from farmed sustainable
forests and was produced with special regard for the environment.
Throughout, the printing and binding have been planned to ensure a sturdy, attractive
publication which should give years of enjoyment.
If your copy fails to meet our high standards, please inform us and we will gladly replace it.

Music Sales' complete catalogue describes thousands of titles and is available in full colour
sections by subject, direct from Music Sales Limited. Please state your areas of interest and
send a cheque/postal order for £1.50 for postage to: Music Sales Limited, Newmarket Road,
Bury St. Edmunds, Suffolk IP33 3YB.

Visit the Internet Music Shop at
http://www.musicsales.co.uk

All You Need Is Love

Words & Music by John Lennon & Paul McCartney

To Coda ⊕

4

CODA

A Hard Day's Night

Words & Music by John Lennon & Paul McCartney

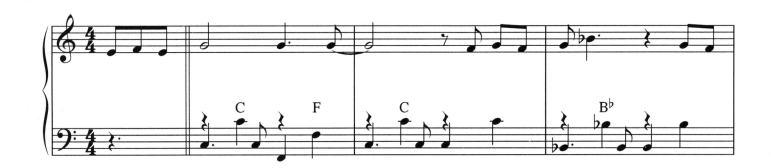

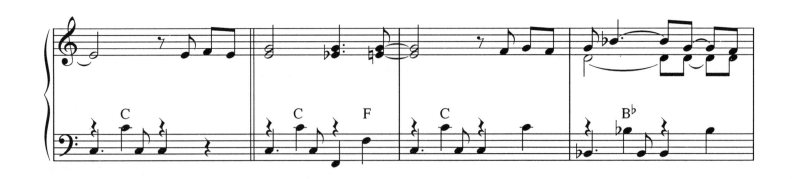

D. %. al Coda

CODA

Eight Days A Week

Words & Music by John Lennon & Paul McCartney

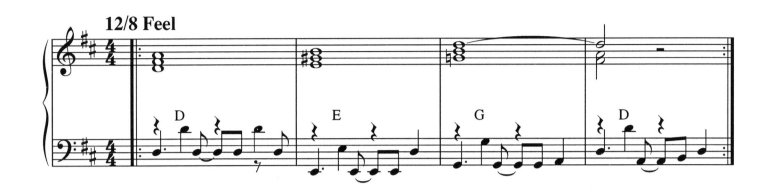

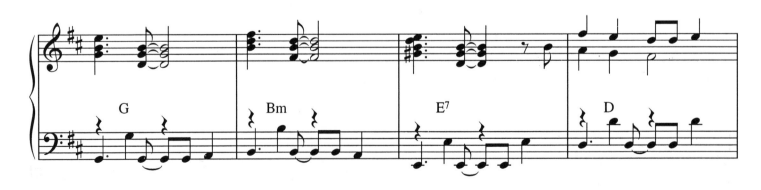

Eleanor Rigby

Words & Music by John Lennon & Paul McCartney

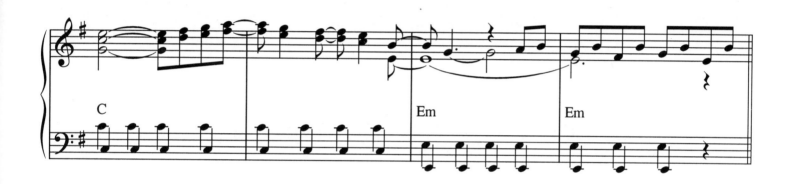

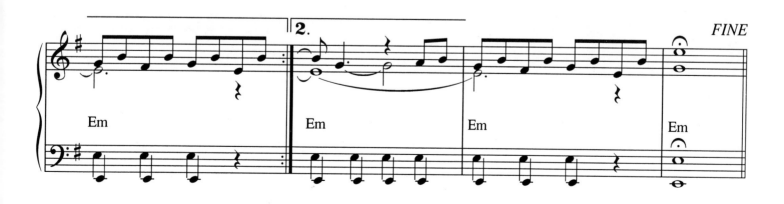

Hey Jude

Words & Music by John Lennon & Paul McCartney

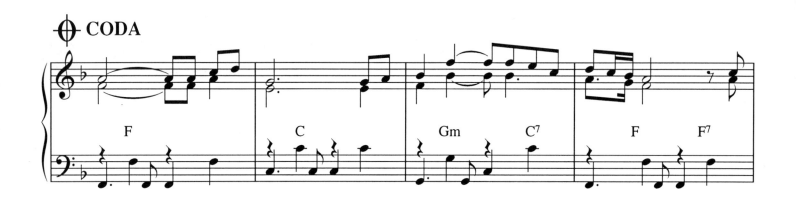

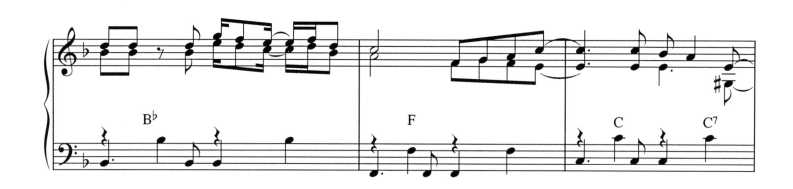

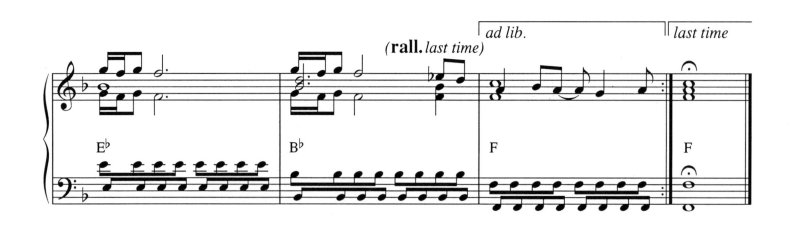

I Want To Hold Your Hand

Words & Music by John Lennon & Paul McCartney

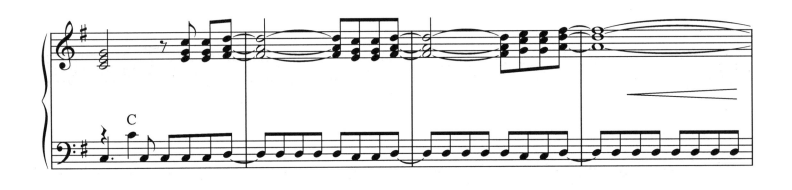

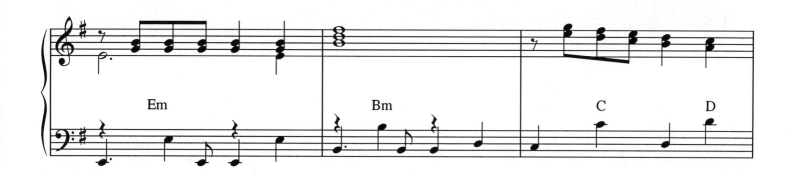

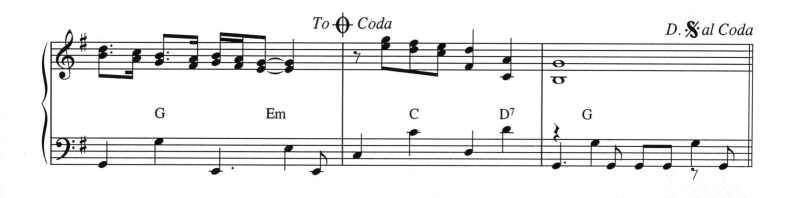

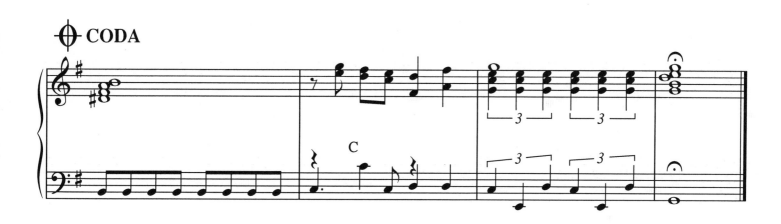

Lucy In The Sky With Diamonds

Words & Music by John Lennon & Paul McCartney

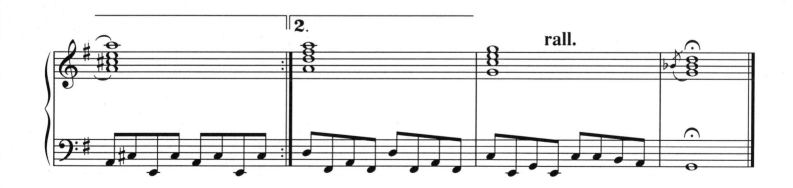

Michelle
Words & Music by John Lennon & Paul McCartney

Nowhere Man
Words & Music by John Lennon & Paul McCartney

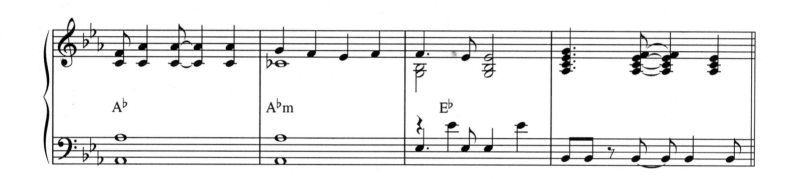

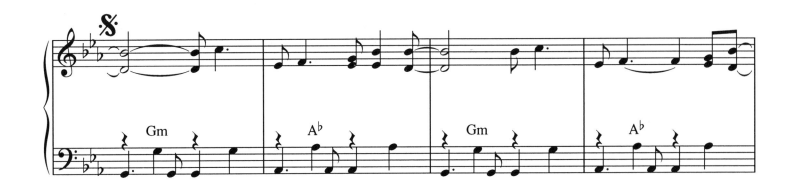

$\oplus$ **CODA**

Norwegian Wood

Words & Music by John Lennon & Paul McCartney

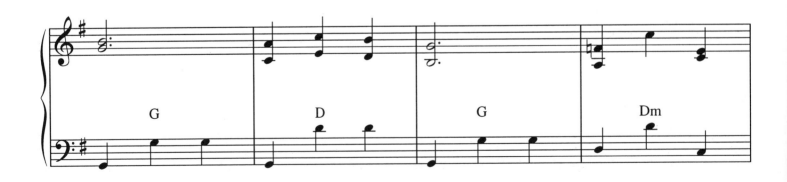

To ⊕ *Coda*   *D.C. al Coda*

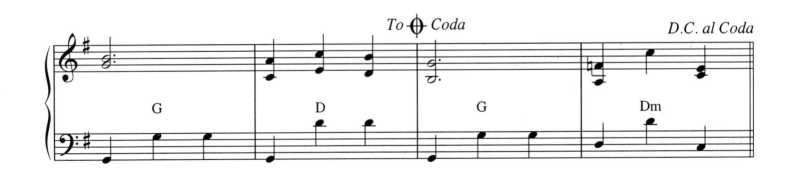

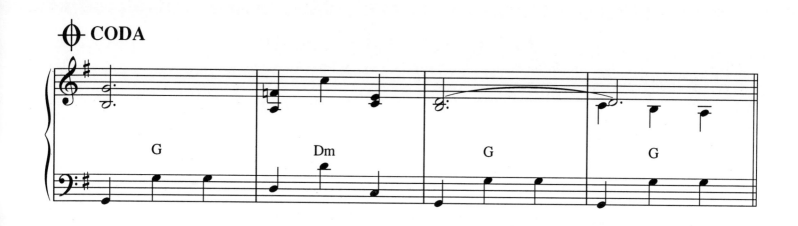

Ob-La-Di, Ob-La-Da

Words & Music by John Lennon & Paul McCartney

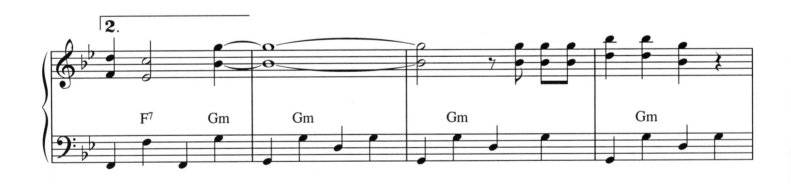

Strawberry Fields Forever

Words & Music by John Lennon & Paul McCartney

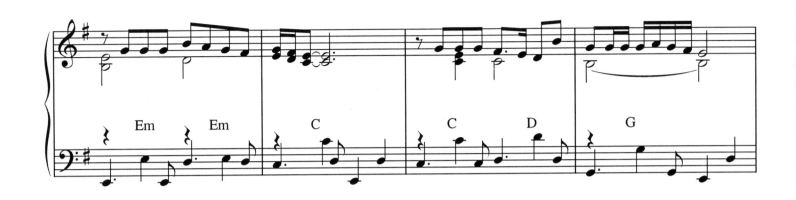

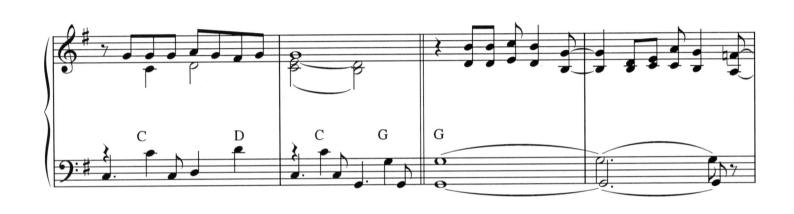

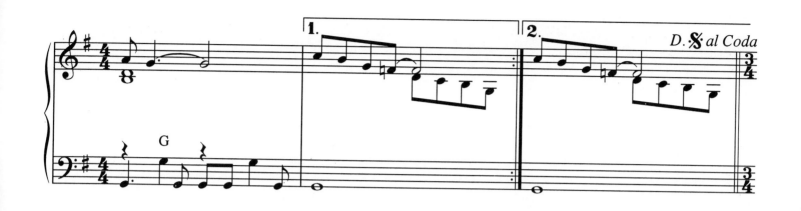

D. $\mathsection$ al Coda

$\oplus$ **CODA**

Yesterday

Words & Music by John Lennon & Paul McCartney

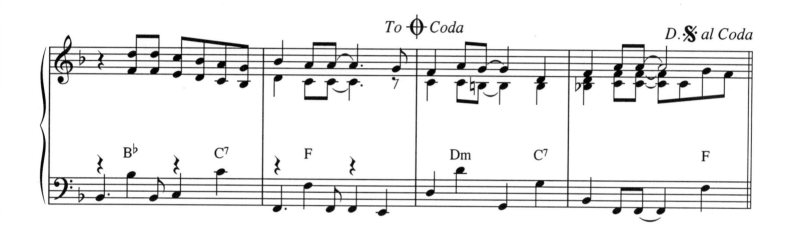

With A Little Help From My Friends

Words & Music by John Lennon & Paul McCartney